Contents

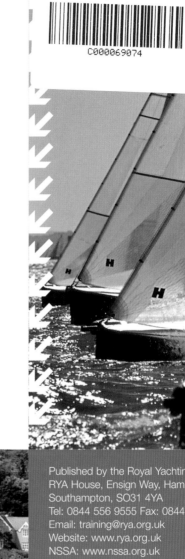

Published by the Royal Yachting Association
RYA House, Ensign Way, Hamble,
Southampton, SO31 4YA
Tel: 0844 556 9555 Fax: 0844 556 9516
Email: training@rya.org.uk
Website: www.rya.org.uk
NSSA: www.nssa.org.uk

© Royal Yachting Association 2009
Reprinted March 2010

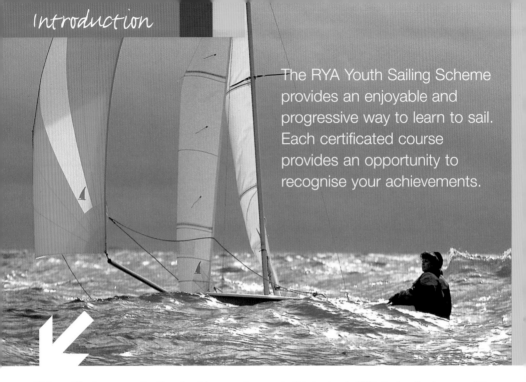

The RYA Youth Sailing Scheme provides an enjoyable and progressive way to learn to sail. Each certificated course provides an opportunity to recognise your achievements.

RYA certificates are a significant achievement. Instructors sign off each skill as you complete it. Once completed, your certificate can be of use in contributing to other areas of your study or activities, such as PE in school, or the Duke of Edinburgh Award Scheme.

The Youth Scheme is usually completed in small dinghies suitable for your size. However, it can also be completed in keelboats and multihulls with some changes to the syllabus (course) e.g. no capsize drill in keelboats.

You can learn to sail well very quickly, provided the equipment is right for you and the challenge suitable. There is provision for guidance and help within the Youth Sailing Scheme, depending on the conditions and what you have to do. In general, you may receive physical help with any part of the syllabus when more strength is required, e.g. on a steep and slippery slipway.

Make sure you can perform all the skills in one course before tackling the next one; otherwise you may waste time re-learning skills, or even fail to complete all of the new course.

In this logbook 'With instruction' means 'Can perform the task with a briefing for the conditions, and physical assistance if necessary'.

In general, courses in the RYA Youth Sailing Scheme are of a minimum length of two days or an equivalent series of sessions. They may be run over a longer period, especially if you have not sailed since your last course. Sailing is a sport which gets better with practice, and you should try to sail between courses whenever possible. Practice makes perfect!

Sailors who are unable to complete parts of the syllabus due to a disability may still receive a certificate, endorsed as necessary e.g. 'needs assistance with capsize drill'.

Advanced Racing

Intermediate Racing

| Seamanship Skills | Day Sailing | Sailing with Spinnakers | Start Racing | Performance Sailing |

Stage 4

Stage 3

Stage 2

Stage 1

Following completion of Stage 4, you can further develop your skills through the five Advanced Modules. You may choose any module according to the area of sailing which interests you; start racing, day sailing, seamanship skills or performance sailing, the choice is yours... Details of these modules are also available in RYA publication G4, the National Sailing Scheme Syllabus and Logbook. You can choose either logbook to continue to record your progress. Additionally there are two further race training courses available to help you improve your performace at club racing level. Happy sailing.

PRACTICAL

Rigging

Can assist with rigging a boat.

Launching & recovery**

Can launch a dinghy and get under way with instruction.

Can secure boat to trolley.

Can assist with recovery and stowage of dinghy and gear.

Ropework

Can tie a figure of eight knot and cleat a halyard.

Sailing techniques & manoeuvres

Can be a responsive crew under instruction*.

Can steer when sailing and being towed.

Can steer on a reach and go about (reach to reach).

Understands the effect of basic boat controls.

Understands the basic principles of stopping, controlling speed and getting out of irons.

Can paddle or row (with sprit, paddle or oars).

Can call for assistance.

Clothing and equipment

Can put on personal buoyancy correctly.

Is confident in the water wearing personal buoyancy.

Capsize recovery

Understands the importance of staying with the boat**.

SAILING BACKGROUND

Can name basic parts of a boat (i.e. hull, mast, rudder, tiller, centreboard, sheets etc).

Understands what action to take to help those in distress.

Understands local hazards.

Understands how to prepare for a tow.

Clothing and equipment

Understands personal safety - and knows what to wear for sailing (including head and footwear).

Meteorology

Has knowledge of wind direction.

*   *not singlehanders*
**   *not keelboats*

ALL SECTIONS COMPLETED

Instructor's signature   Centre stamp

By the end of this introductory course, you will have a basic understanding of how a boat sails, and some experience of steering and handling the boat. Stages 2, 3 and 4 will complete your introduction to the sport in easy stages.

RYA
youth
SAILING SCHEME

STAGE 1

Attach completed certificate here

This is to certify that

_____

has completed all the requirements of this award to the standards laid down in the RYA Youth Sailing Scheme.

SIGNED _____
                                    Principal/Chief Instructor

OF _____
                                    Recognised Training Centre

DATE _____

SPECIAL ENDORSEMENTS _____

_____

Y1

PLACE SIGNATURE HERE

PRACTICAL
Rigging

Can put a boat head to wind for rigging.

Can rig a dinghy.

Launching & recovery**

Understands how to manoeuvre a trolley clear of other boats and overhead cables.

Can launch and recover a small dinghy in an offshore wind.

Ropework

Can tie a round turn and two half hitches and a reef knot.

Sailing techniques & manoeuvres

Can control speed, and stop by lying-to.

Can get out of irons.

Can go about (close reach to close reach).

Can crew a boat effectively*.

Can sail a shallow triangle across the wind under supervision (gybing optional).

Understands the principles of:

The five essentials.

Returning to a beach** or pontoon (offshore wind).

Capsize recovery**

Can be scooped in during capsize recovery*.
or
Can right one type of dinghy.

SAILING BACKGROUND
Sailing manoeuvres

Understands the No Go Zone.

Understands what is meant by windward, leeward and gybe.

General

Has knowledge of:

Spars and rigging.

Parts of the sail.

Sail controls and foils.

Offshore and onshore winds.

Telling someone ashore.

The dangers of man made hazards e.g. overhead power lines, weirs.

Rules of the road

Has knowledge of Port / Starboard rule.

Meteorology

Understands several ways of finding wind direction.

Clothing and equipment

Can choose and correctly adjust a personal buoyancy aid.

Understands what to wear.

*   *not singlehanders*
** *not keelboats*

ALL SECTIONS COMPLETED

Instructor's signature   Centre stamp

By the end of this course, you will have a range of sailing skills and background knowledge, and be well on the way to being a confident small boat sailor.

STAGE 2

Attach completed certificate here

This is to certify that

_____

has completed all the requirements of this award to the standards laid down in the RYA Youth Sailing Scheme.

SIGNED _____

Principal/Chief Instructor

OF _____

Recognised Training Centre

DATE _____

SPECIAL ENDORSEMENTS _____

_____

Y2

PLACE SIGNATURE HERE

PRACTICAL

Rigging, launching & recovery**

Can rig, launch and recover in an onshore wind.

Can reef a dinghy ashore according to weather conditions.

Can store a dinghy ashore.

Ropework

Can tie a bowline, clove hitch and rolling hitch.

Sailing techniques & manoeuvres

Can demonstrate the basic principles of the following:

The five essentials - sail setting, balance, trim, course made good and centreboard.

Sailing on all points of sailing on a triangular course.

Tacking upwind.

Gybing from a training run.

Righting a small capsized dinghy as helm/crew**.

Coming alongside a moored boat.

Prepare for/take up tow from power craft.

Picking up a mooring.

Racing

Understands the course and starting procedure.

SAILING BACKGROUND

Manoeuvres

Understands how to recover a man overboard.

Understands the points of sailing.

General

Understands how a sail works - basic aerodynamics.

Knows basic terminology for use afloat (windward, leeward, bear away, luff up).

Understands the importance of clear communication aboard.

Understands lee shore dangers and sailing in close company with other water users.

Understands advice to inland sailors for coastal sailing.

Knows the importance of personal safety and telling someone ashore.

Understands the dangers of hypothermia and the importance of first aid training.

Rules of the road

Knows the basic rules of the road - Port/Starboard, windward boat and overtaking boat.

Meteorology

Knows how to obtain a weather forecast.

Understands Beaufort Wind Scale.

Knows when to reef.

Clothing and equipment

Understands the importance of:

Personal safety equipment.

Boat buoyancy.

Basic safety equipment e.g. anchor, paddle, bailer.

*   *not singlehanders*
**   *not keelboats*

ALL SECTIONS COMPLETED

Instructor's signature   Centre stamp

Having completed Stage 3 you will be able to
sail in any direction and rig and launch your
boat. Your skills and knowledge mean that you
can regard yourself as a sailor, not a beginner.

STAGE 3

Attach completed certificate here

This is to certify that

_____

has completed all the requirements of this
award to the standards laid down in the
RYA Youth Sailing Scheme.

SIGNED _____
                                    Principal/Chief Instructor

OF _____
                                    Recognised Training Centre

DATE _____

SPECIAL ENDORSEMENTS _____

_____

Y3

PRACTICAL
Rigging & launching

Can rig, launch and recover in any wind direction.

Can set up a boat according to weather conditions using sail and rig controls e.g. mast rake, reefing.

Ropework

Knows the uses of and can tie:

Figure of eight, round turn and two half hitches, reef knot, bowline, clove hitch, rolling hitch, sheet bend.

Sailing techniques and manoeuvres

Can demonstrate:

Sailing techniques and manoeuvres from Stage 3 in a crewed boat.

Communicate effectively as helm and crew.

Effective use of the 5 essentials by helm and crew afloat including use of tell-tales.

Recovering a man overboard.

Returning to a beach,** jetty or mooring safely in any wind direction.

SAILING BACKGROUND

Has knowledge of:

IRPCS.

Beaufort Scale.

Synoptic charts.

Tidal ebb and flow.

Spring and neap tides.

Knows how to recover from total inversion**.

COASTAL (OPTIONAL)

Can apply practical sailing techniques and manoeuvres on tidal waters.

Sailing background

Can apply the IRPCS afloat.

Has basic knowledge of IALA buoyage, how to use tide tables and how to find the direction of tidal streams.

*   *not singlehanders*
**   *not keelboats*

ALL SECTIONS COMPLETED

Instructor's signature   Centre stamp

A Stage 4 certificate means that you have the skills to sail a double-handed boat as crew or helm, and solve a variety of problems afloat. Passing this course is the natural entry point for the advanced courses.

STAGE 4

This is to certify that

Attach completed certificate here

has completed all the requirements of this award to the standards laid down in the RYA Youth Sailing Scheme.

SIGNED _____
Principal/Chief Instructor

OF _____
Recognised Training Centre

DATE _____

COASTAL ENDORSEMENT

SIGNED _____

OF _____

DATE _____

SPECIAL ENDORSEMENTS _____

_____ Y4

Advanced skills

Once you have learned to helm and crew a small boat, all sorts of opportunities in sailing are open to you. As in all sports, practice is essential if you are to improve your skills and the best way to become a good sailor is to sail a variety of types of boats in different conditions.

Having practised your skills one of the best ways to try a different type of sailing is to take another RYA course.

Following Stage 4, you have a choice of Advanced Modules in the RYA National Sailing Scheme. All of these can be run in two days, but they can take place over a longer period of time. Each course will introduce you to a different type of sailing, and may involve other classes of boat, depending on what is available locally.

Why not share your skills with your friends? The Assistant Instructor award is available to those with suitable skills and experience - talk to the Senior Instructor at your club.

Further details of the National Sailing Scheme are available in RYA publication G4, the National Sailing Scheme Syllabus and Logbook.

PRACTICAL
Ropework

Can tie a fisherman's bend and sheet bend.

Can do heat sealing & whipping.

Launching and recovery

Can leave and return to beach, jetty or mooring - windward/leeward shore.

Sailing techniques & manoeuvres

Is able to:
heave to ☐
reef afloat ☐
recover MOB ☐
be towed ☐
anchor† ☐
sail backwards ☐
sail in adverse circumstances**† ☐

Knows how to prepare road trailer and secure ashore.

COASTAL OPTION

Capable of practical application of skills in coastal waters.

Can use local tide tables.

Understands Rule of Twelfths and is aware of tidal streams.

Has a basic understanding of charts and important symbols.

SAILING BACKGROUND
Sailing theory

Understands terminology: windward, leeward, abeam, forward, aft, ahead, astern, to weather, downwind, amidships, quarter, pinching, sailing by the lee, luff, bear away, planing, sternway, broaching.

Knows and can apply the following International Regulations for the Prevention of Collisions at Sea (IRPCS): meeting other sailing vessels, meeting power driven vessels, following or crossing narrow channels, action by stand-on vessel.

Capsize recovery

Knows how to recover from total inversion.

Meteorology

Knows sources of information on weather patterns for day.

Can interpret forecasts and understand local effect.

Aware of Beaufort Scale and changing weather conditions.

Experienced sailor's direct assessment
The candidate must present logged evidence of at least two season's sailing experience. He will satisfactorily complete the practical elements and answer questions on the theory sections. Candidates seeking assessment on coastal waters will demonstrate knowledge from coastal section.

** *not necessarily applicable to keelboats*
† *not necessarily applicable to multihulls*

ALL SECTIONS COMPLETED

Instructor's signature　　　Centre stamp

Learning skills a short step beyond Stage 4; during this course you will polish and test your skills and learn to re-solve problems afloat. The course will give you a solid foundation for the future and enable you to become much more confident and self-sufficient afloat.

RYA
youth
SAILING SCHEME

SEAMANSHIP SKILLS

D13

RYA

Seamanship Skills

This is to certify that ....

has been examined at ....
            Training Centre RYA
and has successfully completed the course
in Dinghies/Keelboats/Multihulls. *

Signed .... *Date* ....
Principal /Chief Instructor

Special endorsements ....
**delete as applicable*

PLACE SIGNATURE HERE

PRACTICAL
Rigging

Can rig boats including spinnakers and trapeze where fitted.

Launching and recovery

Understands how to launch boats with open transoms / racks.**†

Sailing techniques & manoeuvres

Sail as crew or helm using equipment to advantage.

Perform spinnaker hoist, gybe and drop as crew or helm.

Understands and can sail best course downwind.

Capsize recovery

Perform capsize recovery with spinnaker.

Know how to recover from inversion.**

SAILING BACKGROUND
Racing

Has knowledge of courses for type of boat.

Sailing theory and background

Understands the concept of apparent wind.

Understands the effect of hullshapes on performance.

Sources of information and apply rig set-up for different conditions.

Experienced sailor's direct assessment

The candidate will complete all of the practical elements demonstrating a competent, purposeful and confident approach to an instructor. He will satisfactorily answer questions on the theory section afloat and ashore.

**   *not necessarily applicable to keelboats*
†   *not necessarily applicable to multihulls*

ALL SECTIONS COMPLETED

Instructor's signature   Centre stamp

A very short syllabus which probably packs the most fun of all the RYA courses. Everything you need to know to enjoy modern, three-sail boats.

RYA
youth
SAILING SCHEME

SAILING WITH SPINNAKERS

D15

R/A

Sailing with Spinnakers

This is to certify that ....

has been examined at ....
Training Centre R/A

*and has successfully completed the course
in Dinghies/Keelboats/Multihulls.* *

Signed .... *Date* ....
Principal /Chief Instructor

Special endorsements ....
*delete as applicable

PLACE SIGNATURE HERE

PRACTICAL
Rigging

Can prepare and equip a boat for cruising including safety and navigation equipment, clothing and food.

Can stow gear correctly.

Sailing techniques & manoeuvres

Can plan and undertake a day sail including a consideration of pilotage / navigation and collision avoidance.

Can use anchor to effect lee shore landing and departure.**†

Adverse conditions

Is able to self rescue following total inversion.**

Understands how to improvise in the event of gear failure.

SAILING BACKGROUND
Sailing theory & background

Has knowledge of boat handling in strong winds and difficult conditions (practical where possible).

First aid

Basic knowledge of first aid.

First aid certificate holders are exempt from this item.

Navigation

Can plan a day cruise in coastal waters, including knowledge of:

Publications i.e. charts, tide tables.
Navigation instruments.
Use of GPS.
Tidal heights and streams, rule of twelfths.
Decision making including planning alternatives.
Magnetic compass: variation / deviation
Chart work.
Use of transits and bearings to steer and position fix.
Recording position and dead reckoning.

Meteorology

Knows sources of information on weather patterns. Understands high and low pressure systems. Has awareness of changing weather conditions. Understands simple synoptic charts.

Experienced sailor's direct assessment

The candidate must present logged evidence of at least two season's sailing experience. The candidate will complete all of the practical elements demonstrating a competent, purposeful and safe approach. He will also answer questions on the theoretical sections and whenever possible demonstrate skills satisfactorily afloat and ashore.

** *not necessarily applicable to keelboats*
† *not necessarily applicable to multihulls*

ALL SECTIONS COMPLETED

Instructor's signature   Centre stamp

If you sail at a coastal location you can explore the local sailing area, as well as developing your passage planning and decision making skills for small boat cruising. Basic pilotage and dealing with windy conditions are also covered.

DAY SAILING

RYA youth
SAILING SCHEME

D14

Day Sailing

This is to certify that ....

has been examined at ....

Training Centre RYA

and has successfully completed the course in
Dinghies/Keelboats/Multihulls*.

Signed .... Date ....
Principal /Chief Instructor

Signed .... Date ....
Principal /Chief Instructor

Special endorsements ....
*delete as applicable

PLACE SIGNATURE HERE

PRACTICAL
Rigging

Can rig any type of boat, including spinnaker and trapeze (if equipped).

Sailing techniques & manoeuvres

Can make best possible use of crew and equipment to sail efficiently on all points of sailing in a variety of conditions, including symmetric or asymmetric spinnakers.

Can spot and use wind shifts and gusts to effect best course up / down wind.

Can perform capsize recovery with spinnaker.**

Knows how to recover from total inversion.

SAILING BACKGROUND
Sailing theory

Understands how to make use of wind variations and tidal eddies.

Has an understanding of hull shape and rig types including their effect on performance.

Understands planing and effect of rails.

Meteorology

Knows sources of information on weather patterns for the day.

Understands main characteristics of high and low pressure systems and simple interpretation of synoptic charts.

Has awareness of changing weather conditions.

Experienced sailor's direct assessment

The candidate must present logged evidence of at least two season's sailing experience. The candidate will complete all of the practical elements demonstrating a competent, purposeful and safe approach to sailing performance boats. He will also answer questions on the theoretical sections and whenever possible demonstrate skills satisfactorily afloat and ashore.

**   *not applicable to keelboats*

ALL SECTIONS COMPLETED

_____

Instructor's signature   Centre stamp

Improve your boat handling and confidence in performance boats. This is an opportunity to be coached and practise your helming and crewing and work on a smooth, fluent sailing performance with or without the spinnaker.

PERFORMANCE SAILING

Performance Sailing

This is to certify that ....

has been examined at ....
Training Centre

and has successfully completed the course
in Dinghies/Keelboats/Multihulls. *

Signed .... *Date* ....
Principal /Chief Instructor

Special endorsements ....
'delete as applicable

Two day course to introduce novice sailors to racing at clubs

PHYSICAL PREPARATION

Has knowledge of food as a fuel.

Has knowledge of keeping hydrated.

BOAT PREPARATION

Has knowledge of how to rig a racing dinghy.

Has knowledge of availability of class tuning guides.

BOAT HANDLING

Understands:
How to make best use of 5 essentials as crew and helm.

How to round marks.

BOAT SPEED

Understands how to alter sail controls both round the course and for differing conditions.

TEAMWORK

Understands the requirements to develop a good partnership.

STRATEGY & METEOROLOGY

Obtain and understand a simple weather forecast.

Has knowledge of clear air, gusts and lulls.

RACING RULES

An introduction to the racing rules of sailing and an understanding of the basic right of way rules.

TACTICS

Has knowledge of basic boat on boat situations.

STARTS

Has knowledge of transits.

Can demonstrate the basics of starting.

ALL SECTIONS COMPLETED

Instructor's signature

Centre stamp

The start line for enjoying club racing. All you need to know to get round the course and lay the foundations for winning. This is a predominantly practical course.

START RACING

This is to certify that

_____

has completed and passed the

Start Racing Syllabus

CLUB _____

DATE _____

RYA RACING COACH (signature) _____

NAME _____

Five day programme to develop / improve the racing technique and knowledge for racing at club level

PLACE SIGNATURE HERE

MENTAL PREPARATION

Has a basic understanding of how stress affects sailing.

PHYSICAL PREPARATION

Has knowledge of stretching exercises to be used after sailing.

Understands importance of hydration and nutrition during racing.

BOAT PREPARATION

Has knowledge of how to use a tuning guide and set a boat up for specific conditions.

Understands how to prepare a boat for club racing to include: hull, spars, sails, foils, fittings, rigging and control lines.

BOAT HANDLING

Has knowledge of how to steer the boat without a rudder.

Understands the principles involved in slow speed handling including stopping, accelerating and sailing backwards.

BOAT SPEED

Has knowledge of basic aerodynamics - how a sail works, how to power up or de-power the rig, weather and lee helm.

Understands how to set up the boat for a range of conditions.

TEAMWORK

Understands how to divide up the roles around the course.

Understands how to divide up the jobs in the boat.

STRATEGY & METEOROLOGY

Understands clean air, gusts and lulls.

Understands how to interpret a weather forecast in relation to the sailing venue.

RACING RULES

Has good knowledge of Part 2 and definitions of the racing rules.

Understands how to sail by racing rules.

TACTICS

Understands boat on boat tactics, lee bow situation, how to cover and break cover, importance of clear air.

STARTS

Understands bias and how to assess it.

Has knowledge of how to protect a gap to leeward, hold boat on line (hovering), accelerate off the line.

ALL SECTIONS COMPLETED

Instructor's signature   Centre stamp

A five day programme to build on your basic racing skills and develop greater awareness of the key principles of starting boat handling, boat speed, strategy and tactics. This is a predominantly practical course.

INTERMEDIATE RACING

This is to certify that

_____

has completed and passed the

Intermediate Racing Syllabus

CLUB _____

DATE _____

RYA RACING COACH (signature) _____

NAME _____

A five day programme to develop racing skills and knowledge for racing at Open meetings

MENTAL PREPARATION

Has knowledge of process and outcome goals.

PHYSICAL PREPARATION

Understands importance of hydration and nutrition – pre, during and post race.

Understands effects of sleep deprivation.

BOAT PREPARATION

Understands how to improve foil finish, optimise boat to class rules, use a tuning guide.

Understands how to check trailers – wheel bearings, legality and safety prior to travelling.

BOAT HANDLING

Understands importance of teamwork and coordination, how to race train by oneself.

Understands principles of steering with sails and balance and demonstrate these principles in taking penalty turns.

BOAT SPEED

Understands relevance of sail controls and effects on the sail.

Understands how to change 'gears' in different conditions while on the water.

Understands how to vary the tuning guide for different conditions and how to create own tuning guide and post race analysis sheet.

TEAMWORK

Understands effective race analysis and race and training goals.
Can communicate effectively and can react to changing circumstances.

STRATEGY & METEOROLOGY

Can create a race strategy prior to going afloat based on weather forecast, tide tables, etc.

RACING RULES

Have a good knowledge of the racing rules. Sail by the racing rules.

TACTICS

Has knowledge of holding a lane upwind, boat on fleet tactics, attacking and controlling situations.

Understands boat on group tactics, overtaking and defending tactics, covering, different approaches to marks and when to gybe or bear away set.

STARTS

Understands pre start rules.

Can protect a gap to leeward, hold the boat on the line (hovering), use transits.

Has knowledge of various start sequences, recall signal and starting penalties.

ALL SECTIONS COMPLETED

_____

Instructor's signature   Centre stamp

Developing skills in preparation for open meetings
and higher level competition. This is a
predominantly practical course.

ADVANCED RACING

This is to certify that

_____

has completed and passed the

Advanced Racing Syllabus

CLUB _____

DATE _____

RYA RACING COACH (signature) _____

NAME _____

Racing is an exciting and sociable way to develop your sailing. Starting out can be a little daunting, so these notes highlight the key areas you need to consider in learning to race, and give guidance to help make your racing fun and rewarding.

There are a number of ways to go racing:

SAILING CLUBS

Most racing in the UK is run by clubs, during the evening or weekends. Some larger clubs may have a youth section and many run introductory race training sessions.

As a club member you may be able to hire a boat, or sail with another member, but in many clubs you need to have use of your own boat. Lots of clubs run regular courses and training to help sailors to improve at all levels. They may also host 'open meetings' for a particular class of boat (see below).

Clubs that run youth coaching are often granted Champion Club status. This means that they have a good quality safe and effective race training programme which enthuses and develops young sailors. These clubs have strong links to the RYA Junior and Youth squads.

CLASS ASSOCIATIONS

Members of these organisations sail the same class of boat. There will be an active programme of race meets or open meetings around the country and a national championship to decide the best sailor of that class. Most class members have a home sailing club, but many travel to attend open meetings.

RYA SQUADS

The RYA runs zone and national squads across the country to help develop talented young racers across the junior and youth age groups. Sailors train and race in the following recognised classes:

Zone Squads - (normally under 13/14)
Optimist, Topper, Cadet, Mirror, Windsurfer

Junior Squads - (normally under 16)
Optimist, Topper, Cadet, Mirror, Bic Techno 293OD, Hobie Dragoon

Youth Squads - (under 19)
Laser Standard, Laser Radial, 420, 29er, Neil Pryde RS:X, Multihull

Each squad has specific training programmes and selection criteria. Further details may be found in the 'Racing' section of the RYA website or via the RYA Racing Department.

These squads are underpinned by the Volvo RYA Champion Club Programme and together form the national pathway for developing and supporting talented young racers. Further information may also be found in the RYA Youth and Junior Racing guide, available from the Racing Department or your local High Performance Manager.

GETTING STARTED IN A CLUB

The majority of sailing is run at approximately 1400 sailing clubs across the UK situated on waters ranging from large ponds to the open sea. Most welcome new members; you should talk first to a committee member to find out about training courses and opportunities to sail.

Many clubs are listed in your local phone book but you can also find club information at www.rya.org.uk or www.rya.org.uk/vcc

Choosing the right club will be an individual decision but here are some questions to consider:

- Do they run training for novice sailors?
- Is the sailing area safe for novices?
- What classes of dinghy do they race and when?
- How much is membership and what does it include?
- Do I need to buy a boat?

RYA Training Centres and clubs will provide boats when you learn to sail, but to develop your skills you can also sail with someone else or buy your own boat. Sailing with an experienced person is a really good way to learn and many clubs run schemes to introduce new sailors into the club.

If you do decide to buy a boat the best way to select one is to find out what classes are sailed at your club and which boat is best for your size and ability.

WHAT INFORMATION IS AVAILABLE TO HELP ME?

1. RYA Website www.rya.org.uk

As governing body for the sport of sailing, the RYA provides a comprehensive listing of clubs and classes, as well as all the RYA recognised Training Centres, where you can learn to sail.

2. Websites & Magazines

Yachts and Yachting:
www.yachtsandyachting.co.uk

Dinghy Sailing Magazine:
www.dinghysailingmagazine.co.uk

3. RYA publications

The RYA is internationally renowned for producing quality books, films and leaflets to assist sailors at all levels. To access these either phone and ask for a brochure or look on our website: www.rya.org.uk

4. Sailing Books

The RYA produces a wide range of books and DVDs to help you master the skills of sailng such as:

G3 the Beginners Sailing Handbook
G12 the Advanced Sailing Handbook
G32 Go Sailing
G45 Go Sailing Activity Book
G42 Go Cruising
G44 Optimist Handbook
Start Sailing DVD
Better Sailing DVD

Just log on to www.rya.org.uk and order online.

DATE	CLASS OF BOAT	HOURS EXPERIENCE		ACTIVITY AND WEATHER CONDITIONS		CENTRE/CLUB
		HELM	CREW	TYPE OF COURSE OR ACTIVITY	MAX WIND SPEED	INSTRUCTOR/COACH

Personal log

DATE	CLASS OF BOAT	HOURS EXPERIENCE		ACTIVITY AND WEATHER CONDITIONS		CENTRE/CLUB
		HELM	CREW	TYPE OF COURSE OR ACTIVITY	MAX WIND SPEED	INSTRUCTOR/COACH

Personal log

DATE	CLASS OF BOAT	HOURS EXPERIENCE		ACTIVITY AND WEATHER CONDITIONS		CENTRE/CLUB
		HELM	CREW	TYPE OF COURSE OR ACTIVITY	MAX WIND SPEED	INSTRUCTOR/COACH

Personal log

DATE	CLASS OF BOAT	HOURS EXPERIENCE		ACTIVITY AND WEATHER CONDITIONS		CENTRE/CLUB
		HELM	CREW	TYPE OF COURSE OR ACTIVITY	MAX WIND SPEED	INSTRUCTOR/COACH

NSSA

www.nssa.org.uk

NSSA exists to promote sailing as part of the educational experience of young people.

JOIN THE NATIONAL SCHOOLS SAILING ASSOCIATION AND TAKE PART IN ANY OF OUR EVENTS.

- Area and Regional Championships and Series.

- NSSA National Championships for the more experienced sailor.

- NSSA Keel Boat Match Racing Championship, to develop keel boat racing skills.

- NSSA National Youth Regatta Week aimed at young sailors of all levels including a specialist Rookie fleet, but with serious racing on several courses.

- An international competition held in September. Teams are chosen from performances at the Championships Regatta and local events.

- Team racing is hotly contested in Toppers, which are provided. Winning teams are invited to represent the NSSA at the RYA Youth Team Racing Championships.

- School Sailing Matters - a quarterly magazine for members.

- NSSA curriculum support materials available online to members - a 'must' for all teachers, trainers, coaches, interested parents and helpers. Lots of ideas and practical guidance.

- The NSSA is working very closely with the RYA to promote youth sailing. RYA Training Centre status can be developed in partnership with NSSA.

The NSSA is a charitable trust, reg. no. 285904. Our income is from subscriptions, English Sports grants and fees from advertisements and flyer distribution.

Hon Secretary

Mel Ellis
email: secretary@nssa.org.uk

For NSSA membership please contact:

Rachel Bell
email: membership@nssa.org.uk

4 Green Moss, Oakthwaite Road, Windermere, Cumbria LA23 2BB

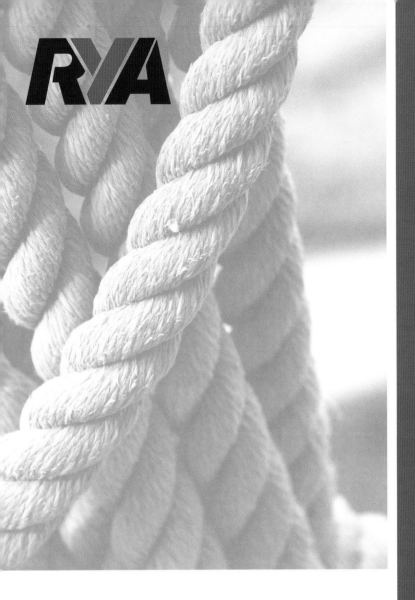

MEMBERSHIP

Promoting and Protecting Boating

www.rya.org.uk

JOIN NOW
online at
www.rya.org.uk

IT'S ALL ABOUT YOU AND THE BOATING YOU DO

RYA MEMBERSHIP APPLICATION

RYA — Be part of it

One of boating's biggest attractions is its freedom from rules and regulations. As an RYA member you'll play an active part in keeping it that way, as well as benefiting from free expert advice and information, plus discounts on a wide range of boating products, charts and publications.

To join the RYA, please complete the application form below and send it to The Membership Department, RYA, RYA House, Ensign Way, Hamble, Southampton, Hampshire SO31 4YA. You can also join online at www.rya.org.uk, or by phoning the membership department on +44 (0) 23 8060 4159. Whichever way you choose to apply, you can save money by paying by Direct Debit. A Direct Debit instruction is on the back of this form.

	Title	Forename	Surname	Gender	Date of Birth
Applicant ❶					/ /
Applicant ❷					/ /
Applicant ❸					/ /
Applicant ❹					/ /

Address

Post Code

E-mail Applicant ❶	
E-mail Applicant ❷	
E-mail Applicant ❸	
E-mail Applicant ❹	

Home Tel

Day Time Tel

Mobile Tel

Type of membership required (Tick Box)

Personal Annual rate £43 or **£39 if paying by Direct Debit**

Family* Annual rate £63 or **£59 if paying by Direct Debit**

Under 21 Annual rate £14 or **£11 if paying by Direct Debit**

* Family Membership. 2 adults plus any under 21s all living at the same address. Prices valid until 31/12/2011

One discount voucher is accepted for personal and junior memberships, and two discount vouchers are accepted for family membership.

Save money by completing the Direct Debit form overleaf

Please number up to three boating interests in order, with number one being your principal interest

Yacht Racing	Yacht Cruising	Dinghy Cruising
Personal Watercraft	Sportboats & RIBs	Dinghy Racing
Powerboat Racing	Canal Cruising	Windsurfing
	River Cruising	Motor Boating

IMPORTANT In order to provide you with membership benefits the details provided by you on this form and in the course of your membership will be maintained on a database. If you do not wish to receive information on member services and benefits please tick here ☐ . By applying for membership of the RYA you agree to be bound by the RYA's standard terms and conditions (copies on request or at www.rya.org.uk)

Signature

Date / /

Source Code

Joining Point Code

GET MORE FROM
YOUR
BOATING
SUPPORT THE
RYA

PAY BY DIRECT DEBIT – AND SAVE MONEY

Instructions to your Bank or Building Society to pay by Direct Debit

Please fill in the form and send to:
Membership Department, Royal Yachting Association, RYA House, Ensign Way, Hamble,
Southampton, Hampshire SO31 4YA.

Name and full postal address of your Bank/Building Society

To the Manager .... Bank/Building Society

Address ....

.... Postcode

Name(s) of Account Holder(s)

Branch Sort Code

☐ ☐ – ☐ ☐ – ☐ ☐

Bank/Building Society Account Number

☐ ☐ ☐ ☐ ☐ ☐ ☐ ☐

Originator's Identification Number

9	5	5	2	1	3

RYA Membership Number (For office use only)

Instructions to your Bank or Building Society
Please pay Royal Yachting Association Direct Debits from the account detailed in
this instruction subject to the safeguards assured by The Direct Debit Guarantee.
I understand that this instruction may remain with the Royal Yachting Association
and, if so, details will be passed electronically to my Bank/Building Society.

Signature(s)

Date: D D / M M / Y Y Y Y

RYA
Be part of it